Saving the Seas
for the Purple and Green

Written & Illustrated by

NANCY CARLISLE

Saving the Seas for the Purple and Green: A Story of Cleaning up the Ocean
Published by Sage Green Press
Denver, CO

Copyright ©2022 by Nancy Carlisle. All rights reserved.

No part of this book may be reproduced in any form or by any mechanical means, including information storage and retrieval systems without permission in writing from the publisher/author, except by a reviewer who may quote passages in a review.

All images, logos, quotes, and trademarks included in this book are subject to use according to trademark and copyright laws of the United States of America.

ISBN: 978-1-7361182-1-4
JUVENILE FICTION / Science & Nature / Environment

Publisher's Cataloging-in-Publication data

Names: Carlisle, Nancy, author.
Title: Saving the seas for the purple and green : a story of cleaning up the ocean / written and illustrated by Nancy Carlisle.
Description: Denver, CO: SageGreen Press, 2022. | A girl loves the tide pools she sees on her runs by the ocean, but notices garbage amongst the colorful creatures she finds there. Conservationists help clean up and educate about the dangers trash poses to ocean life. | Resources included. | Glossary included.
Identifiers: ISBN: 978-1-7361182-1-4
Subjects: LCSH Tide pool ecology--Juvenile fiction. | Marine resources conservation--Juvenile fiction. | Restoration ecology--Juvenile fiction. | Conservation of natural resources--Juvenile fiction. | BISAC JUVENILE FICTION / Science & Nature / Environment | JUVENILE FICTION / Animals / Marine Life
Classification: LCC PZ7.1 .C37 Sav 2022 | DDC [E]--dc23

Cover and Interior design by Victoria Wolf, wolfdesignandmarketing.com. copyright owned by Nancy Carlisle. Illustrations by Nancy Carlisle.

QUANTITY PURCHASES: Schools, companies, professional groups, clubs, and other organizations may qualify for special terms when ordering quantities of this title. For information, email sagegreenpress@gmail.com or visit nancycarlislebooks.com.

All rights reserved by Nancy Carlisle and Sage Green Press.
Printed in the United States of America.

I was so moved when I saw the display of art made from ocean
plastic by Washed Ashore at the Denver Zoo in 2014.

It inspired me to write this book.

Since then,
I have learned of many organizations and people working to
eliminate plastic pollution from our oceans and waterways.

This book is dedicated to all of you.

Violet, curious and outdoorsy, loves nature.

She likes to run freely through the woods to the beach.

Her favorite colors are purple and green. In the woods, she runs past purple flowers, berries, green trees, and grasses.
She sees the purple and green that she loves the best in the sea stars and anemones in the TIDE POOLS at the beach.

TIDE POOL LIFE

Sea stars typically have five arms but can have up to twenty-three arms that they can regenerate. They are KEYSTONE PREDATORS, meaning that they play an important role in maintaining the balance in the cycle of life in their ecosystem. An ecosystem is similar to a neighborhood where animals and plants live together. The keystone predator is needed to keep the number of other creatures at a healthy level for the size of their neighborhood.[1]

When the tides are in, sea anemones look like beautiful flowers. The "petals" are actually tentacles to sting prey (human fingers will only feel a gentle tug, which isn't harmful). Sea anemones are carnivorous. They eat meat such as crabs or sea urchins. The giant green ones live for more than 100 years.[2]

The stars cling to rocks and shimmer in the sunlight.
The anemones' soft tentacles sway with the TIDES.

Today when she finds them, they are not
shimmering and swaying in their
TIDE POOLS. Instead, they are tumbling
and bumping into floating plastic trash!

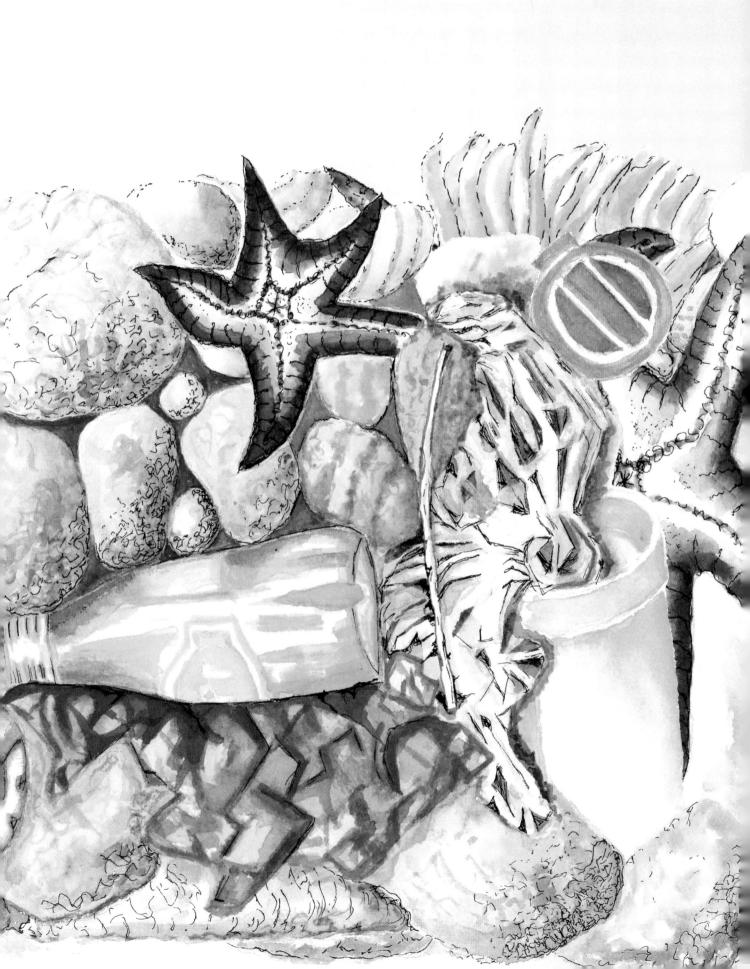

She quickly pulls the trash from the tide pool. Looking to her right, she spies a sea turtle. She knows that sea turtles eat SEA JELLIES and starts to worry. Sea jellies and plastic bags look alike floating in the water. *Could the sea turtle grab a plastic bag, thinking it is a sea jelly, and eat it for lunch?*

A GROWING PROBLEM

Scientists estimate that more than eight million METRIC TONS of plastic are entering our ocean every year. This is equal to dumping the contents of one garbage truck in the ocean every minute! If we keep producing plastics and fail to dispose of them properly, plastics in the ocean will outweigh fish pound for pound by 2050.[3] Eighty percent of ocean trash comes from land; it blows into the streams that flow into the oceans.

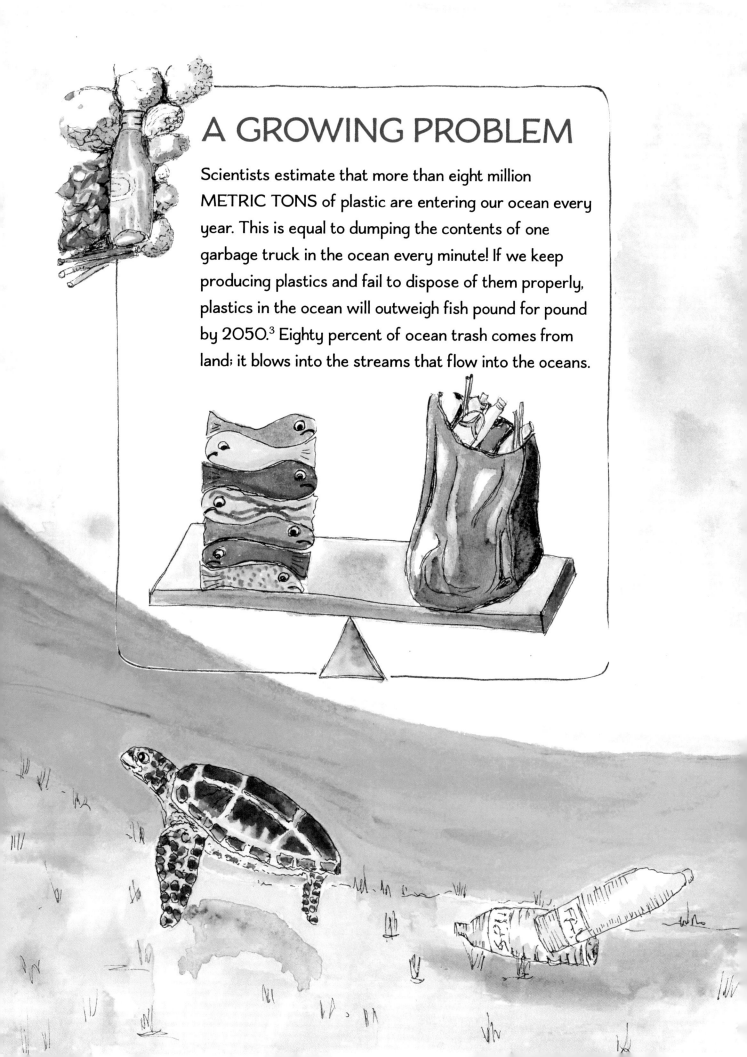

Lost in her thoughts about
the sea turtle, she catches
a flying bag caught on a gust
of wind. *Where did
this come from?*

COMPETITION

After winning first place in an international competition for using upcycled materials, the surfboard created by Taylor Lane, a California surfer and industrial design graduate, sparked a worldwide conversation about ocean pollution. Now teamed with others, he is making a film to highlight the problem and encourage others to act. It will be released in Fall 2022.[4]

A surfer, chasing the bag, runs toward Violet. He is an engineering student collecting trash to make a recycled surfboard to enter in a recycled products contest.

Further up the beach, she sees a mother and son picking up plastic trash on the beach. "What are you going to do with all of that?" she asks. "We'll show you!" they answer with excitement.

RECYCLING

can be UPCYCLING or
DOWNCYCLING. Recycling is
important but should never be the
primary focus of preventing pollution.
It is always better to use less,
waste less, and substitute
sustainable materials like
cardboard for
plastics.[5]

WASHED ASHORE

Washed Ashore, founded by artist and teacher, Angela Haseltine Pozzi, is a non-profit organization in Bandon, Oregon with a mission to build aesthetically powerful art to educate a global audience about plastic pollution in our oceans and waterways and spark positive change in consumer habits. As of 2021, it built 86 sculptures using over 60,000 pounds (30 tons) of waste found on local beaches. They have been exhibited at zoos, botanic gardens, and aquariums across the country. What began as one courageous woman's idea now involves 12,500 people working together.[6]

Together, they walk to a group of people washing and sorting piles of plastic trash by color— blue, yellow, orange, and of course, purple and green. It is a workshop where people turn ocean trash into art to educate the public.

Violet sees a gigantic colorful fish with soulful eyes. She walks closer and discovers that it is made of hundreds of pieces of plastic trash. *Wow, this is really cool but also really sad. I recognize many of the plastic pieces as things I use and throw away, like old flip flops, squirt guns, and bottles.*

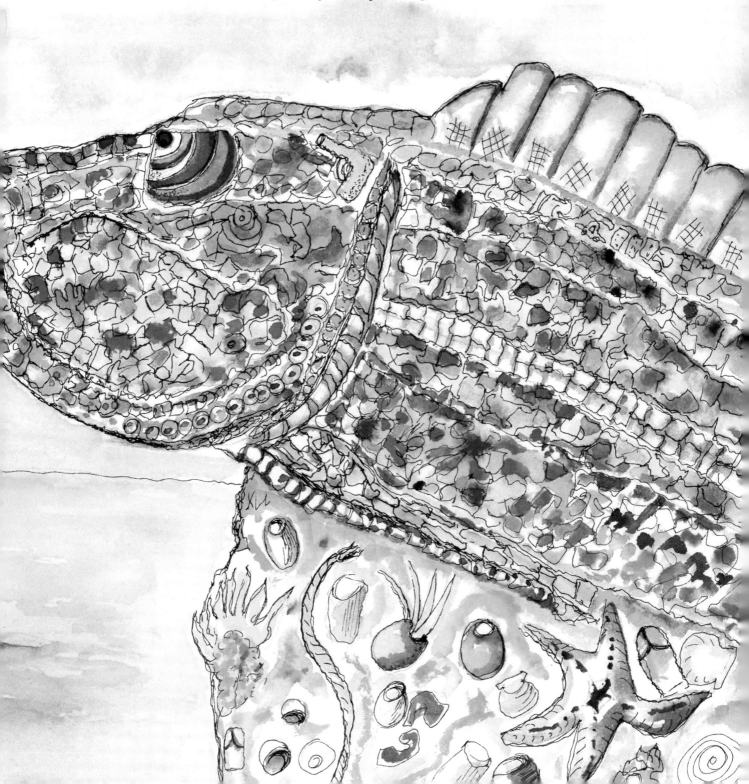

They walk around the workshop, looking at displays and information about plastic in the ocean. They see piles of plastic straws. *Yikes! I didn't know that the plastic straws I use in restaurants end up in the ocean. Maybe I don't really need to use a straw?*

SKIP THE STRAW

There are several websites (see the references) that advocate to "skip the straw." The Skip the Straw movement was started in 2011 by a young boy named Milo. When he was only nine years old, he estimated that 500,000 plastic straws were used in the United States each day. He started a project to enlist restaurants to reduce the use of plastic straws. His project gained attention, and he became a leader in the worldwide discussion about reducing plastic waste. In college, he studied computer programming and mathematics.[7]

Violet reads posters about people who are working to solve the plastic pollution problem. One company developed "edible capsules" of water that athletes can use instead of water bottles when running races. *How cool! It must be like eating a bite of water encased in Jell-O™, and it leaves no waste, she thinks.* Several young engineers, designers, and chemists came up with this idea and started a company.

NOTPLA

Notpla is a business that makes edible drink capsules (called water pods) from seaweed. In April of 2019, 40,000 water pods were handed out to runners at the London Marathon. Moving forward, other marathons are planning to use the water pods too! The company also makes edible containers for condiments like ketchup and mayonnaise and COMPOSTABLE takeout boxes that decompose in four to six weeks in a landfill. Most other COMPOSTABLE takeout boxes require a high temperature composting facility (these facilities aren't available in many locations) or take eighty years to decompose in a landfill.[8]

Another poster describes a business that creates packaging products from mushrooms as a substitute for Styrofoam™. This company was started by young biologists. The products are used for packing furniture and wine bottles and as coolers for shipping products.

Violet sees another poster about a boat sailing around the world piloted by young women studying the problem of plastic in the ocean. *That might be something I could do in a few years.*

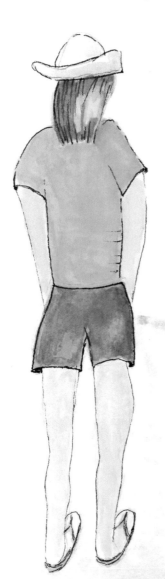

EXXPEDITION

The eXXpedition is an all-female sailing research expedition. In October 2019, they set out to sail around the world for two years with a plan to involve 300 women across 30 voyages. After completing eight voyages, involving 80 women from 28 countries, due to COVID, the focus shifted to virtual events to engage local communities.[10]

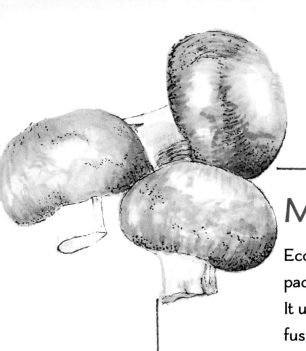

MYCELIUM

Ecovative design is a business that makes packaging materials grown from mushrooms. It uses agricultural waste such as wood chips fused together by a matrix of mushroom roots called MYCELIUM. This material is 100 percent compostable and can be molded to any desired packaging shape.[9]

Violet continues looking at posters. One describes a college student running across the United States to increase awareness of the problem of plastic in the ocean. Another describes a young man who built a floating device to trap plastic waste.

She reads that cities and states are passing laws to regulate the use of plastic; businesses are developing ways to recycle and use less plastic in packaging; and school kids are becoming active advocates for taking care of the environment. There are many ways to make a difference.

Violet sees sunglasses, athletic shoes, backpacks, and other beachwear made from recycled ocean trash. She buys a pair of colorful recycled board shorts just like the surfer was wearing!

Later she thinks, All the people I met or read about today are helping to clean the ocean and reduce the amount of plastic used in the world. I will too. She starts thinking about careers where she could invent, lead, or contribute to making less waste.

AWARENESS

In 2020, Sam Bencheghib ran 3,035 miles across the United States to create awareness of plastic.[11]

At eighteen years old, Dutchman Boyan Slat invented a system to trap plastic before it reaches the seas. The machines are in use in Indonesia, Malaysia, Vietnam, and as of July 2021, in the great Pacific garbage patch.[12]

The problem of plastic in the ocean is big, but as Violet learned, everyone can do something to help, no matter how small. Sometimes it only takes one person with an idea to set a good example and lead at any age.

How can you change your habits to keep the ocean purple, green, and clean for sea anemones, starfish, sea turtles, and the future?

HOW CAN YOU HELP?

Say no to plastics that can't be recycled. Consider alternatives such as cloth, paper, or previously recycled products.

Recycle plastic bottles, cups, and lids. Reuse the plastic that you do use, like plastic grocery bags for trash bags.

When visiting the beach or wilderness, pack out all your trash.

Learn about the environmental impacts of waste on the planet. Share your knowledge with your friends, parents, and teachers. Be a good example to others.

GLOSSARY

COMPOSTABLE: Waste made from natural materials—such as vegetable waste, coffee grounds, eggshells, leaves, paper, and cardboard—which decompose (breaks down) to form soil nutrients and does not pollute the air, water, or land.

DOWNCYCLING: To recycle plastic by making new products of lesser quality such as plastic bags.

KEYSTONE PREDATOR: The keystone predator maintains balance in an ecosystem. For example, if the sea stars died, more barnacles, mussels, or sea urchins would live longer because the sea stars wouldn't be around to eat them. These animals would, in turn, eat more algae, which means small fish would lose their hiding places and then might get eaten by larger fish.

METRIC TON: A metric ton is 1,000 kilograms or 2,025 pounds, or about half the size of a hippopotamus.

MYCELIUM: The part of the mushroom that is usually underground. It looks like threads or rootlets, and it extracts nutrients from the soil.

SEA JELLIES: Often referred to as jellyfish, but they are not a fish. They are an animal with no backbone. They sting their prey and eat fish, crabs, and tiny plants. They can be clear or vibrant in color. Sea turtles eat sea jellies.

TIDES: The rising and falling of the sea level, usually twice a day, which is driven by the cycles of the moon.

TIDE POOLS: Shallow pools of sea water at the ocean's edge. Many tide pools exist separate from the ocean during periods of low tides. Tide pools are home to many animals such as sea stars and sea anemones.

UPCYCLING: This is the process of recycling waste materials, such as plastic trash, into new materials or products of better quality or for better environmental value. Examples include using plastic trash to make shampoo bottles or sunglass frames.

RECOMMENDED READING

The following includes books and websites to provide more information on oceans, trash, and the environment to inspire young people to pursue their ideas.

All the way to the Ocean. Harper, Joel. [The story is also told in a video with the same name found on YouTube (www.allthewaytotheocean.com.)]

Boy and Whale. Gertstein, Mordicai.
Here We Are: Notes for Living on Planet Earth. Jeffers, Oliver.
Little Kids First Big Book of the Ocean. Hughes, Catherine D.
National Geographic Kids Mission: Sea Turtle Rescue. Young, Karen Romano.
One Plastic Bag. Paul, Miranda.
What a Waste: Rubbish, Recycling and Protecting Our Planet. French, Jess.

WEBSITES
https://www.oceanconservancy.org
https://oregontidepooling.com
https://www.plasticpollutioncoalition.org
https://www.sailorsforthesea.org
https://thelastplasticstraw.org
http://www.nationalgeographic.org/topics/resource-library-plastic-pollution/
https://washedashore.org
https://www.thecigarettesurfboard.com/
https://www.youngvoicesfortheplanet.com/
https://www.natgeokids.com/uk/kids-club/cool-kids/general-kids-club/plastic-pollution/

REFERENCES

1   Exploring Rocky Shores of Southern Oregon Coast. n.d. "What Are Those Strange Creatures Clinging to the Rocks During a Low Tide?" Accessed January 10, 2022. https://www.oregontidepooling.com.

2   National Geographic. "Role of Keystone Species in an Ecosystem," September 5, 2019. https://www.nationalgeographic.org/article/role-keystone-species-ecosystem/.

3   World Economic Forum, Ellen MacArthur Foundation, and McKinsey and Company. 2016. "The New Plastics Economy: Rethinking the Future of Plastics." https://emf.thirdlight.com/link/faarmdpz93ds-5vmvdf/@/preview/1?o.

4   The Cigarette Surfboard. n.d. "Using Ciggy Butts & Surfing to Build Ocean Stewardship." Accessed January 10, 2022. https://www.thecigarettesurfboard.com.

5   Cirino, Erica. "'Upcycling' Ocean Plastic Trash Comes into Fashion." The New Humanitarian, August 7, 2017. https://deeply.thenewhumanitarian.org/oceans/articles/2017/08/07/upcycling-ocean-plastic-trash-comes-into-fashion.

6   Washed Ashore: Art to Save the Sea. n.d. "Making Waves in 2022." Accessed January 10, 2022. https://www.washedashore.org.

7   Ecocycle. n.d. "Meet Milo, Founder of Be Straw Free." Accessed January 10, 2022. https://www.ecocycle.org/bestrawfree/about.

8   Notpla. n.d. "We Make Packaging Disappear." Accessed January 10, 2022. https://www.notpla.com.

9   Ecovative. n.d. "We Grow Better Materials." Accessed January 10, 2022. https://ecovative.com.

10 eXXpedition. n.d. "About Us." Accessed January 10, 2022. https://exxpedition.com/about/about-us/.

11 Make a Change World. n.d. "Make a Change." Accessed January 10, 2022. https://makeachange.world.

12 The Ocean Cleanup. n.d. "The Largest Cleanup in History." Accessed January 10, 2022. https://theoceancleanup.com.

13 Hamilton, Lisa Anne, Steven Feit, Carroll Muffett, Matt Kelso, Samantha Malone Rubright, Courtney Bernhardt, Eric Schaeffer, Doun Moon, Jeffrey Morris, and Rachel Labbe-Bellas. "Plastic & Climate: The Hidden Costs of a Plastic Planet." CIEL: Center for International Environmental Law, May 2019. https://www.ciel.org/wp-content/uploads/2019/05/Plastic-and-Climate-FINAL-2019.pdf.

14 McCoy, Jenny. "How Local Restaurants Are Reducing the Environmental Impact of Takeout." *5280: Denver's Mile High Magazine*, November 6, 2020. https://www.5280.com/2020/11/how-local-restaurants-are-reducing-the-environmental-impact-of-takeout/.

15 Boulder County. "Boulder County Recycling Center Completes Major Upgrades," September 28, 2017. https://www.bouldercounty.org/news/boulder-county-recycling-center-completes-major-upgrades-residents-and-businesses-can-now-recycle-more-types-of-plastics/.

ABOUT THE AUTHOR

NANCY CARLISLE is an author and illustrator who writes hopeful books for kids that interweave facts and fiction about the environment and global responsibility. During her 38-year career as a sustainable architect and researcher, her focus was on the environment. She led work nationally and internationally on sustainable and energy efficient buildings and communities and won awards for collaboratively designing award-winning sustainable buildings, a laboratory campus, and improving the energy efficiency of U.S. laboratories.

Since retiring, Nancy has worked as a volunteer teaching English as a Second Language and mentors first generation college students. She is a strong advocate against plastic waste not only because it pollutes our oceans and water but also because it contributes CO2 to our atmosphere.

Nancy enjoys the outdoors and international travel. She is a member of the Society of Children's Book Writers and Illustrators and the Society of Environmental Journalists. She studies botanical illustrating and French language.

END NOTE

I live in Colorado, far from the ocean but near rivers and lakes, that also experience plastic pollution. You have probably seen many pictures of wildlife killed from plastic and are familiar with the ever-expanding litany of statistics about the impact of plastic waste on ocean plants, animals, corals, beaches, and human health. You may not be aware of the CO2 impacts of plastics in the environment. Ninety-nine percent of all plastic comes from fossil fuels. Plastics are one of the most significant and rapidly growing sources of industrial green-house gas.[13] Worldwide, plastics could account for 13% of greenhouse gases by 2050.

In this book I wanted to focus on the positive and reiterate that we all can work to solve the plastic pollution problem. In addition to the examples I mentioned in the book, there are many other people working on finding solutions. Personally, I'd like to give a shout out to restaurants who are trying to innovate to reuse and reduce plastic take-out containers[14] and to cities and waste management companies who are offering composting and increasing recycling for more types of plastic.[15]

I hope people reading this book will use their voices and their purchasing power, to support programs, policies, and products that reduce plastic waste.

Nancy Carlisle
https://nancycarlislebooks.com

ACKNOWLEDGMENTS

Thank you for the support and development of this story: Shelly Wilhelm, My Word Publishing for editing, Victoria Wolf for graphic design\layout. Angela Haseltine Pozzi for inspiration and encouragement. Jeanann and Rich Lungerhausen, Kari Burman, Zoé Hess, Rich and Janet Carlisle, Nancy Reece Jones, for reviews and comments on the original version and many friends and family members for general support.

ALSO BY
NANCY CARLISLE

MIA and the
HUMMINGBIRD

Written &
Illustrated by

NANCY
CARLISLE

A book about social justice and self-discovery.

Available in paperback and eBook at amazon.com.

Made in the USA
Middletown, DE
06 March 2022

62228425R00022